Foundation Certificate Synoptic

Workbook

Tara Askham

Published by Osborne Books Limited
Tel 01905 748071
Email books@osbornebooks.co.uk
Website www.osbornebooks.co.uk

Design by Laura Ingham

Printed by CPI Group (UK) Limited, Croydon, CR0 4YY, on environmentally friendly,
acid-free paper from managed forests.

MIX
Paper from
responsible sources
FSC® C019777

British Library Cataloguing in Publication Data
A catalogue record for this book is available from the British Library

ISBN 978 1911198 048

Contents

Also available from Osborne Books...

Tutorials

Clear, explanatory books written
precisely to the specifications

Wise Guides

Handy pocket-sized study and revision guides

Student Zone

Login to access your free ebooks and
interactive revision crosswords

Download **Osborne Books App** free from the App Store or Google Play Store
to view your ebooks online or offline on your mobile or tablet.

www.osbornebooks.co.uk

Introduction

Qualifications covered

This book has been written specifically to cover the AAT Synoptic Assessment, which is mandatory for the following qualifications:

■ AAT Foundation Certificate in Accounting – Level 2

■ AAT Foundation Diploma in Accounting and Business – Level 2

■ AAT Foundation Certificate in Accounting at SCQF Level 5

This book provides four full Practice Assessments (with answers) to prepare the student for the Computer Based Synoptic Assessments. Further details of the content and structure of the book are shown on page 1.

Osborne Study and Revision Materials

Our materials are tailored to the needs of students studying this unit and revising for the assessment. They include:

■ **Tutorials:** paperback books with practice activities

■ **Wise Guides:** pocket-sized spiral bound revision cards

■ **Student Zone:** access to Osborne Books online resources

■ **Osborne Books App:** Osborne Books ebooks for mobiles and tablets

Visit www.osbornebooks.co.uk for details of study and revision resources and access to online material.

HOW TO USE THIS SYNOPTIC ASSESSMENT WORKBOOK

INTRODUCTION

The AAT Foundation Certificate in Accounting covers a range of foundation accounting and finance skills including double-entry bookkeeping and basic costing, as well as an understanding of purchase, sales and general ledgers. It covers the use of accounting software and the development of professional skills and behaviours needed to contribute effectively in the workplace. Working in accountancy requires good communication skills, IT skills and an understanding of the business environment, all of which are covered by this qualification. The AAT Foundation Certificate in Accounting comprises the following five units:

- Bookkeeping Transactions *
- Bookkeeping Controls *
- Elements of Costing *
- Using Accounting Software *
- Work Effectively in Finance

All of the units within this Foundation Certificate in Accounting are mandatory. Four units are assessed individually in end-of-unit assessments (in the bulleted list above these are indicated with a *). This qualification also includes a synoptic assessment that students sit towards the end of the qualification, which draws on and assesses knowledge and understanding from across four units in the qualification. Using Accounting software is the one unit not assessed within the synoptic assessment.

Students must successfully complete all four of the unit assessments and the synoptic assessment to achieve the qualification.

synoptic assessment coverage

One of the units in this qualification is only assessed through the synoptic assessment. This is 'Working Effectively in Finance'. However, the synoptic assessment for the Foundation Certificate in Accounting also covers three of the other mandatory units and has four assessment objectives (AO). These are detailed below:

AO1 Demonstrate an understanding of the finance function and the roles and procedures carried out by members of an accounting team.

AO2 Process transactions, complete calculations and make journal entries.

AO3   Compare, produce and reconcile journals and accounts.

AO4   Communicate financial information effectively.

synoptic assessment structure

The synoptic assessment for the Foundation Certificate in Accounting is a computer based assessment that is partially computer marked and partially human-marked. The live synoptic assessment is two hours long.

what this books contains

This book provides four full Practice Synoptic Assessments to prepare the student for the live Computer Based Synoptic Assessments. They are based directly on the structure, style and content of the sample assessment material provided by the AAT at www.aat.org.uk.

The AAT sample assessment material provides a breakdown of the marks allocated to each task. This helps students to appreciate the relative importance of each task in the assessment and to plan how long to spend on each task. The Practice Synoptic Assessments in this book also show the mark allocation for each task.

Suggested answers to the Practice Synoptic Assessments are set out in this book.

The AAT recommend that students complete all other assessments before attempting the synoptic assessment and there are restrictions in place to prevent premature scheduling of the synoptic assessment. It is suggested that in order to gain maximum benefit from this book students should not attempt these Practice Synoptic Assessments until they have studied all five units and completed the four unit assessments.

Practice synoptic assessment 1

Information

The total time for this practice assessment is 2 hours.

The total mark for this practice assessment is 100.

The marks for each sub-task are shown alongside the task.

Read the scenario carefully before attempting the questions.

Scenario

The tasks are set in a business situation where the following conditions apply:

- You are employed as an Accounts Assistant in the finance function at JYB Supplies.

- The finance function includes the financial and management accounting teams.

- JYB Supplies uses a manual bookkeeping system.

- Double entry takes place in the general ledger. Individual accounts of trade receivables and trade payables are kept in the sales and purchases ledger as subsidiary accounts.

- The cash book and petty cash book should be treated as part of the double entry system unless the task instructions state otherwise.

- The VAT rate is 20%.

Task 1: 12 marks

You work from 09.00 to 14.00, Monday to Friday of each week. Each finance period is four weeks in duration so you plan your work in a four week cycle.

The work schedules below show the days when routine tasks must be completed and the amount of time each task takes to complete. It is very important that you complete the management accounts tasks by the end of the identified day and the financial accounts tasks by the day and time indicated.

Monthly work schedule – management accounts					
	Monday	**Tuesday**	**Wednesday**	**Thursday**	**Friday**
Week 1	Data gathering (3 hours)	Cost coding (1 hour) Labour cost report (1 hour)			
Week 2		Labour cost report (1 hour)	Labour cost report (1 hour)	Labour cost report (1 hour)	
Week 3	Budget report (2 hours)		Material Cost report (2 hours)		
Week 4			Product cost analysis (1 hour)	Product cost analysis (1 hour)	Variance analysis (2 hours)

Weekly work schedule – financial accounts			
Task	**Task to be completed each week by:**		**Task duration**
	Day	**Time**	
Contact customers	Wednesday	13:00	2 hours
Contact suppliers	Tuesday	11:00	1 hour
Process purchase invoices	Tuesday	14:00	2 hours
Check emails and post cheques	Every day	12:00	1 hour
Prepare payments to suppliers	Friday	10:00	1 hour
Reconcile supplier statements with purchase ledger	Thursday	14:00	2 hours
Process sales invoices	Monday	14:00	2 hours

You are planning your work at the start of the day on Thursday of week 2. You have been asked to complete a non-routine petty cash book task by 10am, which is already on your to-do list.

(a)   Complete your to-do list for today, Thursday of week 2. Refer to the management and financial accounts schedules and list the tasks in order of completion in the table set out below. Write the task descriptions in the column on the right. You can see the list has been started for you.

Choose from the following tasks:

Contact customers	Data gathering
Product cost analysis	Cost coding
Budget report	Prepare payments to suppliers
Contact suppliers	Variance analysis
Process purchase invoices	Process sales invoices
Labour cost report	Material cost report
Check emails and post cheques	Reconcile supplier statements with purchase ledger

Thursday, week 2 to-do list (in order of completion)	
Task 1 09.00 -10.00	Petty cash book
Task 2 10.00 -11.00	
Task 3 11.00 -12.00	
Task 4 12.00 -13.00	
Task 5 13.00 -14.00	

(4 marks)

You are often asked to complete non-routine tasks. However, on one day in each of the four week cycles you are too busy with routine tasks to accept non-routine work.

(b)   Identify on which day in which week you will be the busiest with routine tasks from the management and financial accounts schedules. Enter your answer into the table below.

Week number	Day of the week

(2 marks)

The non-routine petty cash book task in today's to-do list is completing and finalising the petty cash book below for a colleague who has had to attend an urgent meeting.

Petty cash-book

Details	Amount £	Details	Amount £	VAT £	Stationery £	Postage £	Travel £
Balance b/f	150.00	Paper	15.60	2.60	13.00		
		Train fare	26.30				26.30
		Stamps				9.80	
		Balance c/d					
Total		Totals					

(c)   Complete the petty cash book and calculate the balance c/d.

(4 marks)

(d)   What will be the entries in the general ledger?

Select your account names from the following list:

Balance b/f, Balance c/d, Bank, Petty cash book, Value Added Tax, Stationery, Postage, Travel

General ledger

Account name	Amount £	Debit	Credit

(2 marks)

Task 2: 12 marks

JYB Supplies have taken on Sam, a new accounting apprentice. In his first three months he will be spending time with you and learning about the tasks and functions of the accounting department. You have been discussing some of the tasks you perform in your role and ask Sam to make notes on the following:

(a)   In the table below match the tasks to be completed with the appropriate Accountant.

Tasks:

Deals with future income and costs

Deals with financial transactions that have already happened

Prepares budgets

Prepares the financial statements including tax and VAT

Management Accountant	Financial Accountant

(4 marks)

(b)   Match the task with the job role.

(5 marks)

Task

Sales figures report for each sales advisor

Production schedule for the factory

Process invoices received from suppliers

Process cheques received

Prepare employee contracts

Job role

Sales Manager

Human Resources Assistant

Sales Ledger Assistant

Production Manager

Cashier

Purchase Ledger Assistant

You explain to Sam that working as part of a team is essential in accounting.

(c)   Identify from the list below **three** characteristics of an effective team.

(a)	Good communication skills	
(b)	Must have accountancy qualifications	
(c)	Must complete their work before other members of the group	
(d)	Be able to work to deadlines	
(e)	Be able to help others in the group when required	

(3 marks)

Task 3: 12 marks

JYB Supplies have purchased goods from Light Ltd and have received an invoice. They also received a credit note as some faulty goods were returned.

(a)   Check the invoice below and credit note on the next page for accuracy. State any errors found.

(4 marks)

Purchase Invoice

INVOICE

Light Limited
250 Lenton Boulevard
Clifton, CL45 5KG

VAT Reg GB 541 4874 56

invoice to		
JYB Supplies 410 Wrenthorpe Industrial Estate Clifton CL47 6KU	invoice no	96532
	date/tax point	12 July 20-X

Product Code	Description	Quantity	Price	Unit	Total	Discount	Net
MEB5	Matt Emulsion Paint — Blue 5L	70	£7.50	each	£525.00	20%	£420.00

terms
Net monthly
Carriage paid
E & OE

goods total	525.00
VAT	105.00
TOTAL	420.00

Errors on purchase invoice ....

Purchase credit note

CREDIT NOTE	**Light Limited**
	250 Lenton Boulevard
	Clifton, CL45 5KG
	VAT Reg GB 541 4874 56

invoice to		
JYB Supplies	credit note no	CN 2044
410 Wrenthorpe Industrial Estate	date/tax point	25 July 20-X
Clifton		
CL47 6KU		

Product Code	Description	Quantity	Price	Unit	Total	Discount	Net
MEB5	Matt Emulsion Paint — Blue 5L	12	£7.50	each	£90.00	20%	£81.00

Reason for credit: 12 faulty

goods total	81.00
VAT	16.20
TOTAL	97.20

Errors on purchase credit note ....

Your next task is to enter the invoices that follow into the appropriate day book. Your manager has checked the invoices for accuracy and is happy they are all correct.

(b)   Record the invoice in the correct day book by ticking the correct day book.

(a)	Sales day book	
(b)	Sales returns day book	
(c)	Purchases day book	
(d)	Purchase returns day book	

(6 marks)

Purchase Invoice

INVOICE

PWS Supplies
41 Carlthon Hill
Burton BF4 7HY

VAT Reg GB 748 5410 01

invoice to			
JYB Supplies 410 Wrenthorpe Industrial Estate Clifton CL47 6KU	invoice no	INV4514	
	date/tax point	29 July 20-X	

Product Code	Description	Quantity	Price	Unit	Total	Discount	Net
ST012	Step ladder (3 treads)	12	12.20	each	146.40	15%	124.44

terms
Net monthly
Carriage paid
E & OE

goods total	124.44
VAT	24.88
TOTAL	149.32

Purchase Invoice

INVOICE

Working Products
58 Granby Road
Burton BG5 4DS

VAT Reg GB 236 02455 87

invoice to			
JYB Supplies 410 Wrenthorpe Industrial Estate Clifton CL47 6KU	invoice no	269852	
	date/tax point	30 July 20-X	

Product Code	Description	Quantity	Price	Unit	Total	Discount	Net
WPM24	Work platform — medium	30	£18.30	each	£549.00	10%	494.10

terms
Net monthly
Carriage paid
E & OE

goods total	494.10
VAT	98.82
TOTAL	592.92

Date 20-X	Details	Invoice number	Total	VAT	Net
	Totals				

Task 4: 16 marks

At the end of May you have partially prepared JYB Supplies' Purchase ledger control account, as shown below.

Purchase ledger control

Details	Amount £	Details	Amount £
Bank	4,630	Balance b/f	5,410

You now have the totals of the purchase and purchase returns day books and must record the appropriate amounts in the purchase ledger control account.

Purchase returns day book extract

Date 20-X	Details	Total £	VAT £	Net £
May	Total	5,448	908	4,540

Purchase returns day book extract

Date 20-X	Details	Total £	VAT £	Net £
May	Total	960	160	800

(a)   What will the entries be into the purchase ledger control account?

Account name	Amount £	Debit	Credit
Entry from the purchase day book			
Entry from the purchase returns day book			

(4 marks)

(b)   What will the balance carried down in the purchase ledger control account be?

Amount £	Debit	Credit

(2 marks)

Your next task is to reconcile the sales ledger with the balance in the sales ledger control account. These are the balances in the sales ledger on 1 June.

Credit customers	Balances	
	Amount £	Debit/Credit
Carlton Homeworld	9,500	Debit
TYS Supplies	2,510	Credit
Timber plc	1,440	Debit
JB & Son Painters	3,660	Debit
TS Newton	16,926	Debit

You have inserted the balance of the sales ledger control account in the reconciliation statement below.

(c)   Complete the reconciliation statement by:

- inserting the total of the balances in the sales ledger
- calculating any difference

Reconciliation statement	Amount £
Sales ledger control account balance	29,463
Total of the sales ledger balances	
Difference	

(2 marks)

Your supervisor wants to know what may have caused the difference shown in the reconciliation statement.

(d)   Which **two** of the reasons below could explain the difference you calculated in (c) above?

Reasons	
A discount allowed was not entered in a customer's account in the sales ledger	
A credit note was entered twice in the sales ledger control account	
An invoice was entered twice in a customer's account in the sales ledger	
A discount allowed was entered twice in the sales ledger control account	
A receipt was entered twice in a customer's account in the sales ledger	
An invoice was entered twice in the sales ledger control account	

(2 marks)

The list of balances in the sales ledger in (c) on the previous page shows the account of Carlton Homeworld. Your colleague has prepared a draft email to be sent to Mr Jones at Carlton Homeworld to remind them that the balance on their account is overdue.

(e)   Review the draft email and highlight **six** errors. Errors may be wrongly spelt, incorrectly used or technically incorrect.

Hi Mr Jones

Our purchase ledger shows an outstanding balance on your account of £9,050. This has been outstaning for 60 days which has eceeded our 30 day payment terms.

Please can you arrange payments as soon as possable and if you have any questions or queries please do not hesitate to contact me.

Kind regards

(6 marks)

Task 5: 12 marks

JYB Supplies are reviewing their sustainability policy.

(a)   Select which areas of sustainability the following statements refer to.

	Social	Environmental
Using resources that can be reused		
Supporting colleagues		
Reduction of emissions		
Reduce the quantity of printing		
Donation of profits to charity		
Energy saving schemes		

(6 marks)

In line with their commitment to improving the local environment, JYB Supplies recently held an event to raise much needed funds for the local primary school. The Corporate Social Responsibility team is responsible for reporting on the costs of the event. Any variance in excess of 4% of the budget is thought to be significant and should be reported to your manager.

(b)   Complete the table below by:

• Inserting the variance in £

• Inserting adverse or favourable

• Inserting significant or not significant

Event cost performance report

Cost	Budget £	Actual £	Variance £	Adverse/ Favourable	Significant/ Not significant
Entertainment	800.00	835.00			
Food	600.00	623.00			

(6 marks)

Task 6: 24 Marks

Your manager at JYB Supplies has asked you to assist the payroll department today as a member of staff is off sick. You are told that JYB Supplies uses a time-rate method with bonus to pay its direct labour in its factory. The time-rate is £7.90 per hour and a worker is expected to produce 9 units an hour, anything over this and the worker is paid a bonus of £0.60 per unit.

(a) Calculate the basic wage, bonus and gross wage for the four workers in the table below:

Employee name	Hours worked	Units produced	Basic wage £	Bonus £	Gross wage £
Lukasz	36	370			
Samuel	36	320			
James	36	330			
Tom	36	344			

(12 marks)

(b)   In the box below, write a short report for non-finance staff containing:

• A brief introduction outlining the areas you will be covering in the report

• An explanation of what time-rate pay is, giving an example

• An explanation of what piecework is, giving an example

• A description of other types of pay to be considered when making payments to employees

Your report must be clear and structured appropriately.

(12 marks)

Task 7: 12 Marks

You are preparing for the accounting month end at JYB Supplies.

You have been asked to prepare a trial balance from the list of account balances provided below.

(a)   Show whether the amounts will be debits or credits in the trial balance and total the trial balance.

Account name	Amount £	Debit	Credit
Bank (overdraft)	2,600		
Sales	28,704		
Purchases	16,256		
Sales returns	2,900		
Purchase returns	680		
Office equipment	9,300		
Administration expenses	1,008		
Sales ledger control	12,580		
Purchase ledger control	4,630		
Capital	5,680		
Petty cash	250		
Total			

(6 marks)

Your manager informs you that the balance of £1,440 on Timber plc's account needs to be written off as an irrecoverable debt.

(b)   Record the journal entries to be made into the general ledger to record the irrecoverable debt of £1,440. This amount includes VAT at 20%.

Journal

Account name	Amount £	Debit	Credit

(2 marks)

(c)   Record the journal entry to be made into the sales ledger account of Timber plc.

Account name	Amount £	Debit	Credit

(2 marks)

Your manager asks you to balance the following two accounts in the purchase ledger at 31 July 20-X.

(d)   Complete the accounts by:

- Inserting the balance carried down together with the date and details
- Inserting the totals
- Inserting the balance brought down together with the date and details

Fairtown Ltd

Date 20-X	Details	Amount £	Date	Details	Amount £
14 July	Credit note CN41	500.00	1 July	Balance b/f	2,000.00
16 July	Bank	700.00	12 July	Invoice 3245	1,000.00

Smithson Taylor

Date 20-X	Details	Amount £	Date	Details	Amount £
11 July	Credit note 25	103.40	1 July	Balance b/f	645.00
20 July	Bank	645.00	10 July	Invoice INV457	475.30

(2 marks)

Practice synoptic assessment 2

Information

The total time for this practice assessment is 2 hours.

The total mark for this practice assessment is 100.

The marks for each sub-task are shown alongside the task.

Read the scenario carefully before attempting the questions.

Scenario

- You are employed as an accounts assistant in the finance function at Brooklane Garden Centre.

- The finance function includes the financial and management accounting teams.

- Brooklane Garden Centre uses a manual bookkeeping system.

- Double entry takes place in the general ledger. Individual accounts of trade receivables and trade payables are kept in the sales and purchases ledger as subsidiary accounts.

- The cash book and petty cash book should be treated as part of the double entry system unless the task instructions state otherwise.

- The VAT rate is 20%.

Task 1: 12 marks

Brooklane Garden Centre have taken on Tamara, a new accounting apprentice. In the first two months she will be spending time with you and learning about the tasks and functions of the accounting department.

You explain to Tamara that having the right range of interpersonal skills in an accounting role is essential.

(a)   Have a look at the situations below and identify **one** situation where a range of interpersonal skills have been used effectively.

(a) John and Jasmin have been assigned to working on the budgets, John needs information from Jasmin to complete the work but doesn't get on with her and therefore won't ask.	
(b) During a meeting John is discussing the plan for the new month end procedures. Jim has a good idea and interrupts John to suggest his idea.	
(c) Jim has finished producing the sales invoices and knows that Jasmin is struggling to contact all the customers who have not paid on time. Jim checks with his manager to see if he can offer to help Jasmin.	

(1 mark)

(b)   You have just been looking at your job description with your manager. Decide which tasks from the following list refer to the finance function:

(a) Tax computation	
(b) VAT return	
(c) Production schedule	
(d) Coding invoices	
(e) Issuing contracts to new staff	

(3 marks)

(c)   After completing your induction, you are asked to identify from the following list which **two** policies relate to the accounting function?

(a) Data protection	
(b) Whistleblowing	
(c) Quality control in the production department	
(d) Manual handling for lifting heavy packages	

(2 marks)

(d)   Brooklane Garden Centre have purchased goods from Michelle Proctor Ltd and have received two invoices.

Check the invoices against the purchase orders on the next two pages for accuracy. State any errors found.

(6 marks)

PURCHASE ORDER

BROOKLANE GARDEN CENTRE

No 02486

Date 21 March 20-X

28 Steinbeck Street, Granby, BG3 8JY

To: Michelle Proctor Ltd

Please supply: 20 Square Top Round Base Plastic Planters (Product code LSTR064)

30 Square Plastic Wood Effect Planters (Product code SPWE410)

INVOICE

Michelle Proctor
26 Ashton Close
Granby, BH8 5TF

VAT Reg GB 578 7489 01

invoice to		
Brooklane Garden Centre **28 Steinbeck Street** **Granby** **BG3 8JY**	invoice no	005896
	date/tax point	25 March 20-X

Product Code	Description	Quantity	Price	Unit	Total	Discount	Net
LSTR064	Square Top Round Base Plastic planters	30	4.60	each	138.00	15%	103.50
PWE410	Square Plastic Wood Effect planters	30	5.50	each	165.00	15%	123.75

terms			
Net monthly	**goods total**		£248.46
Carriage paid	**VAT**		£49.69
E & OE	**TOTAL**		£298.15

Errors on purchase invoice ....

PURCHASE ORDER
BROOKLANE GARDEN CENTRE

No 02498
Date 23 March 20-X

28 Steinbeck Street, Granby, BG3 8JY

To: Michelle Proctor Ltd

Please supply: 16 bags of Golden Gravel Decorative Stone (Product code GGDS698)

10 bags of Naturally Rounded Decorative Gravel (Product code NRDG01471)

INVOICE

Michelle Proctor
26 Ashton Close
Granby, BH8 5TF

VAT Reg GB 578 7489 01

invoice to

Brooklane Garden Centre
28 Steinbeck Street
Granby
BG3 8JY

invoice no	005896
date/tax point	27 March 20-X

Product Code	Description	Quantity	Price	Unit	Total	Discount	Net
AGDS698	Amber Gravel Decorative Stone	16	£132.00	each	2,112.00	20%	1,689.60
NRDG01471	Naturally Rounded Decorative Gravel	16	£131.00	each	2,096.00	20%	1,676.80

terms
Net monthly
Carriage paid
E & OE

goods total	£3366.40
VAT	£673.28
TOTAL	£2693.12

Errors on purchase invoice ....

Task 2: 12 marks

You have been asked to explain the importance of solvency to Tamara.

(a)   Which of the following tasks affect the solvency of the business?

(a) Stock valuation	
(b) Bank reconciliation	
(c) Banking cheques received	
(d) Be able to work to deadlines	

(2 marks)

(b)   If the business wants to improve the working capital position, which option would you choose?

(a) Customers pay earlier	
(b) Pay rent earlier	
(c) Pay the National Insurance contributions of employees to HMRC earlier	
(d) Pay suppliers earlier	

(1 mark)

(c)   Identify which of the following improves the smooth running of an organisation, improves solvency and is a legal requirement.

(7 marks)

A sustainability policy including details of the new car sharing scheme	
Petty cash procedures	**smooth running of an organisation**
Make sure credit customers pay on time	
Electronic planner of staff holidays to ensure staff absences are evenly spread	**improves solvency**
Pay the PAYE and National Insurance Contributions to HMRC	
Pay VAT due	**is a legal requirement**
Avoid having to pay overtime to staff	

practice synoptic assessment 2 **29**

(d) A colleague, Jasmin, has nearly finished her AAT Level 2 course and has been offered a promotion in the management accounts team. This will involve assisting the management accountant in preparing the management accounts using Excel. Identify **two** suggested CPD activities suitable for Jasmin.

(a)	Enrol onto AAT Level 3	
(b)	Complete an Excel online course	
(c)	Attend a tax seminar	
(d)	Complete a Microsoft Word course	

(2 marks)

Task 3: 12 marks

(a) You have been asked to enter the transactions below into the appropriate side of the cash book and balance off the cash book.

Receipts from credit customers

Wenlock Building Society 68 Clifton Road, Arnold, AF6 2BE	date **27 July 20-X**	97-76-54

Pay **Brooklane Garden Centre** only

Two thousand, four hundred and ten pounds only ——— £ 2,410.00

Account payee only

L Harris Ltd

L Harris

210114   12 36 17 08   20-60-50

BACS REMITTANCE ADVICE	FROM: Michelle Proctor Ltd 26 Ashton Close Granby BH8 5TF
TO Brooklane Garden Centre 28 Steinbeck Street Granby BG3 8JY	date: 28 July 20-X

date	your reference	our reference	payment amount
28 July 20-X	INV004002	PO1425	£980.60

TOTAL £980.60

THIS AMOUNT HAS BEEN PAID BY BACS CREDIT TRANSFER DIRECTLY INTO YOUR BANK ACCOUNT

Receipts for cash payments

Brooklane Garden Centre
Received cash with thanks for goods bought. From: Askham Ltd, a customer without a credit account. £66 including VAT

Cash book – debit side

Details	Cash £	Bank £	VAT £	Trade Receivables £	Cash sales £
Balance b/f	254.36				

(4 Marks)

(b)   Using your answers to (a) above, calculate the cash balance.

£ [   ]

(1 Mark)

(c)   The bank account had a balance b/f at the beginning of the month of £450.60 on the credit side. Bank payments totalled £4058.60. Using your answers to (a) above, calculate the closing bank balance.

£ [   ]

(1 Mark)

(d)   Will the bank balance calculated in (c) above be a debit or credit balance?

Debit	
Credit	

(2 Marks)

(e)   State whether the transactions below will be posted to the DEBIT side of the cash book or the CREDIT side of the cash book.

	Debit	Credit
Payment to HMRC for VAT of £3,484		
Debit card receipt of £540 from a trade receivable		
Receipt from HRMC for £410		
Debit card payment of £140 to a trade payable		

(4 Marks)

Task 4: 16 marks

(a)   Brooklane Garden Centre has just been informed that a credit customer, Murray Ltd, have ceased trading. Here is Murray Ltd's account in the sales ledger, all amounts include VAT.

Murray Ltd

Date 20-X	Details	Amount £	Date 20-X	Details	Amount £
1 July	Balance b/f	960.50	14 July	Credit note 0236	65.80
16 July	Invoice 2546	2,478.90			
17 July	Invoice 2590	205.70			

(1)   Use the journal to record the entries in the general ledger to write off the net amount, VAT amount and the total amount.

Journal

Account name	Amount £	Debit	Credit

(3 Marks)

(2)   Show whether the errors below will cause an imbalance in the trial balance.

	Will cause an imbalance	Will not cause an imbalance
The vehicle expenses have been debited with £12,451. This should have been posted to the vehicles account		
The balance on the rent received account has been calculated incorrectly		
Rent received of £565 has been recorded as £656 in the rent received account only		
Interest received has been posted to the rent received account		

(4 marks)

(b) On 31 July a partially completed trial balance had a credit balance of £90,620 and a debit balance of £102,649.

(1) The accounts below have not been entered into the trial balance. Complete the table below to show whether each balance will be a debit or a credit in the trial balance.

Account name	Original balance £	Debit	Credit
Purchase returns	2,906		
VAT Control (owing to HMRC)	5,680		
Bank interest received	58		
Bank (overdrawn bank balance)	3,970		
Sales returns	585		

(5 marks)

(2) What will the totals of each column of the trial balance be after entering the above balances from task (b)?

Account name	Debit	Credit
Totals		

(1 mark)

(3) Your colleague has asked you to review an email to be sent to a credit customer as their account is now overdue. Review the draft email and highlight **three** errors. Errors may be wrongly spelt, incorrectly used or technically incorrect.

Email
Hi Mr Templin
Our sales ledger shows an outstandng balance on your account of £10,245. This has been outstanding for 90 days which has exeeded our 30 day payment terms.
Please can you arange payments as soon as possible and if you have any queries please do not hesitate to contact me.
Kind regards

(3 marks)

Task 5: 12 marks

Jim tells you that Brooklane are trying to become a more sustainable company:

(a)   From the list below what would improve sustainability?

(a) Driving for two hours to attend a meeting	
(b) Holding the meeting via skype	
(c) Using recyclable plant holders	
(d) Ensuring customers are treated equally	
(e) Promote a cycle to work scheme	
(f) Print all accounting correspondence and file in the accounts office	

(3 marks)

Brooklane are trying to ensure that overtime is only worked where necessary. Management are analysing current pay and have asked you to calculate the pay for three members of staff who work in the department where plants are grown and maintained. Employees working in this department are paid a time-rate of £14.20 per hour for a 36 hour week. Any employee working in excess of 36 hours per week is paid an overtime rate of £21.20.

(b)   Calculate the basic wage, overtime and gross wage for the week for the three employees in the table below.

Name	Hours worked	Basic wage £	Overtime £	Gross wage £
Sam Stepton	40			
Tanveer Mahmood	42			
Kelly Johnstone	35			

(9 marks)

Task 6: 24 marks

Jasmin asks you to calculate the inventory valuation from the following information:

- The garden centre has 150 pots at £3.60 per unit
- During the month, 70 pots are received at £3.80 per unit
- The following week 180 pots are issued

(a) Calculate the cost of issue and closing inventory for each valuation method.

Method	Cost of issue £	Closing inventory £
FIFO		
LIFO		
AVCO		

(12 marks)

(b) In the box below, write a short report for non-finance staff containing:

- A brief introduction outlining the areas you will be covering in the report
- An explanation of how LIFO and FIFO issues are valued (at oldest or most recent purchase price)
- An explanation of how closing inventory is valued for LIFO and FIFO (at oldest or most recent purchase price)
- A description of how AVCO is calculated

Your report must be clear and structured appropriately.

(12 marks)

Task 7: 12 marks

(a)   You have just finished entering transactions into the day books and are now ready to transfer the information into the double entry bookkeeping system. Jasmin informs you she has already posted the entries from the cash book and petty cash book.

Purchases day book

Date 20-X	Supplier	Invoice number	Gross £	VAT £	Net £	Plants £	Pots £
3 July	Midway Suppliers	54201	876	146	730	470	260
6 July	Peterborough Plants	INV6945	11,436	1,906	9,530	7,840	1,690
8 July	Skegby Suppliers	PI 4009	972	162	810	170	640
Totals			13,284	2,214	11,070	8,480	2,590

(1)   Transfer the entries from the day books into the general ledger.

Account name	Amount £	Debit	Credit

(5 marks)

(2)   Transfer the entries from the day book into the purchase ledger.

Account name	Amount £	Debit	Credit

(3 Marks)

(b)   You now have the totals of the sales and sales returns day books and must record the appropriate amounts in the sales ledger control account.

Sales day book extract

Date 20-X	Details	Total £	VAT £	Net £
July	Total	19,764	3,294	16,470

Sales returns day book extract

Date 20-X	Details	Total £	VAT £	Net £
July	Total	3,720	620	3,100

What will the entries be into the sales ledger control account?

	Amount £	Debit	Credit
Entry from the sales day book			
Entry from the sales returns day book			

(4 marks)

Practice synoptic assessment 3

Information

The total time for this practice assessment is 2 hours.

The total mark for this practice assessment is 100.

The marks for each sub-task are shown alongside the task.

Read the scenario carefully before attempting the questions.

Scenario

* You are employed as an accounts assistant in the finance function at Steinbeck Storage Solutions.

* Steinbeck Storage Solutions manufactures storage solutions.

* The finance function includes the financial and management accounting teams.

* Steinbeck Storage Solutions uses a manual bookkeeping system.

* Double entry takes place in the general ledger. Individual accounts of trade receivables and trade payables are kept in the sales and purchases ledger as subsidiary accounts.

* The cash book and petty cash book should be treated as part of the double entry system unless the task instructions state otherwise.

* The VAT rate is 20%.

Task 1: 12 marks

You have worked at Steinbeck Storage Solutions for 6 months and have just had a review with your manager, Liam. You mentioned that you would like to be more involved in the credit control functions of the business. Liam agrees this would be a good idea and some training relating to customer services and letter writing together with enrolling onto an AAT Level 2 course would be beneficial.

You log into the online training system to identify relevant training opportunities.

(a) Select **two** suitable CPD courses that would benefit you.

(a)	Reporting requirements of corporation tax	
(b)	Telephone training	
(c)	Microsoft Word training	
(d)	Understanding PAYE	
(e)	Conflict resolution	

(2 marks)

You work with a number of departments and deal with various accounting tasks. Part of your role is to ensure that relevant mail received to the accounting department is distributed correctly.

(b) Match the documents to the finance function.

(5 marks)

Documents

Invoice from a supplier

Supplier Statement

Cheque from credit customer with a remittance advice attached

Signed contract of employment

Letter from HMRC with new tax code for an employee

Finance function

Payroll

Purchase ledger

Human resources

Sales Ledger

Your next task is to enter the documents below into the appropriate day book. Your manager has checked the documents for accuracy and is happy they are all correct.

(c)   Record the document in the correct day book by ticking the correct day book:

(a)	Sales day book	
(b)	Purchase returns day book	
(c)	Purchases day book	
(d)	Sales returns day book	

(1 mark)

Purchase credit note

CREDIT NOTE

Woodborough Ltd
60 Newmarket Lane
Wollaton, WL5 2JP

VAT Reg GB 697 7840 74

invoice to

Steinbeck Storage Solutions
53 Maclean Industrial Estate
Beeston
BH6 5RS

credit note no   CN 067

date/tax point   30 July 20-X

Product Code	Description	Quantity	Price	Unit	Total	Discount	Net
MEB5	Hardwood	10	£17.50	each	£175	20%	£140.00

Reason for credit:
wrong type of wood issued

goods total	£140.00
VAT	£28.00
TOTAL	£168.00

Purchase credit note

CREDIT NOTE	LYB Newton & Son Ltd
	47 Stockhill Lane
	Bramcote, BR45 7UE
	VAT Reg GB 201 7036 01

invoice to		credit note no	01240
Steinbeck Storage Solutions 53 Maclean Industrial Estate Beeston BH6 5RS		date/tax point	31 July 20-X

Product Code	Description	Quantity	Price	Unit	Total	Discount	Net
CAB451	Small cabinets	6	£163.20	each	£979.20	20%	£783.36

Reason for credit:		
damaged during transit	goods total	£783.36
	VAT	£156.67
	TOTAL	£940.03

(d)   Record the documents into the day book below and total the day book.

Date 20-X	Details	Credit note number	Total £	VAT £	Net £
	Totals				

(2 marks)

(e) Match the following documents to the appropriate day books:

(2 marks)

Document

Invoice issued to a credit customer

Invoice received from a supplier

Day book

Sales day book

Purchase returns day book

Cash book

Sales return day book

Purchases day book

Task 2: 12 marks

Every few weeks the computer system prompts you to change your password.

(a)   Identify the best type of password:

(a) A password that is easy to remember for example your date of birth	
(b) A password that combines letters and numbers	
(c) A password that combines letters, numbers, uppercase and special characters	

(1 mark)

(b)   A number of policies and procedures are in place at Steinbeck Storage Solutions. Which **one** of the following is not likely to be relevant to the accounting function?

(a) Guidance for lifting heavy items	
(b) Data protection	
(c) Sustainability policy	
(d) Whistle blowing policy	

(1 mark)

Within the Credit Control Department you have been asked to chase outstanding customer payments. When you phone David at Jonathan & Son Ltd, he tells you they will make payment but they are awaiting payment from a customer who your company also deals with, called BHY & Son, and asks you for the Director's personal mobile number as this will mean they can pay your bill.

(c)   Identify what action you should take.

(a) Give him the Director's work mobile number instead	
(b) Give him the number to ensure the company gets paid	
(c) Give out the email address instead	
(d) Refer to your supervisor as this is confidential information you are being asked to disclose	

(1 mark)

(d) The stakeholder of a business is likely to be interested in accounting information. Match the stakeholder to the most appropriate accounting information.

(3 marks)

Stakeholder

Accounting information

Financial accounts for the year

Bank

Stock balance

Investors

VAT return

HM Revenue and Customs

Cash book

(e) Which **three** are fundamental principles of ethics in the workplace?

(a)	Integrity	
(b)	Objectivity	
(c)	Confidence	
(d)	Effectiveness	
(e)	Professional competence	
(f)	Motivation	

(3 marks)

(f) Which **three** tasks would a financial accountant carry out?

(a)	Producing year-end accounts	
(b)	Preparing budgets	
(c)	Preparing VAT returns	
(d)	Calculating the costs of products	
(e)	Preparing tax computations	
(f)	Preparing labour cost analysis	

(3 marks)

Task 3: 12 marks

Today you have been asked to finish preparing an invoice that has been partially completed, in relation to the purchase order below. Liam tells you that the business offers Mapperley Pine Centre a 10% trade discount and a 6% prompt payment discount for payment within seven days.

(a)   Use the information provided to complete the invoice.

PURCHASE ORDER		
MAPPERLEY PINE CENTRE	**No** 021452	
	Date 3 March 20-X	

Carlton Road, Nottingham, MJ5 6LK

To: Steinbeck storage solutions

Please supply: 72 Unfinished pine shelf kit (Product code UPSK2563) @ £6.00 per unit
12 Pine brackets (Product code PB2410) @ £3.20 per unit

Sales invoice

INVOICE

Steinbeck Storage Solutions
53 Maclean Industrial Estate
Beeston, BH6 5RS

VAT Reg GB 870 1247 78

invoice to			invoice no	1240
Mapperley Pine Centre Carlton Road Nottingham MJ5 6LK			date/tax point	5 March 20-X

Product Code	Description	Quantity	Price	Unit	Total	Discount	Net
						10%	

terms		
Net monthly	**goods total**	
Carriage paid	**VAT**	
E & OE	**TOTAL**	
6% prompt payment discount for payment within 7 days		

(8 marks)

You receive a cheque from Mapperley Pine Centre on 10 March, having taken advantage of the prompt payment discount.

(b) How much will the cheque be for?

£ [   ]

(1 mark)

You have also received a cheque for £2,702.99 from NJK Ltd with no remittance advice. Calculate which transactions the payment relates to and select the transactions that are missing. The customer's account is shown below.

Date 20-X	Details	Amount £	Date 20-X	Details	Amount £
1 July	Balance b/f	901.00	20 July	Credit note 050	36.88
14 July	Invoice 601	74.69	21 July	Bank	864.12
16 July	Invoice 658	1,780.50	23 July	Credit note 064	416.33
22 July	Invoice 701	2,639.10	24 July	Credit note 066	10.80
24 July	Invoice 740	908.31			

(c) Circle the three transactions that have not been included in the payment.

Credit note 066	Invoice 601	Credit note 064
Invoice 658	Credit note 050	Balance b/f
Invoice 701	Invoice 740	Bank

(3 marks)

Task 4: 16 marks

Below is the bank statement and cash book for July.

Bank statement

Date 20-X	Details	Paid out £	Paid in £	Balance £	
1 July	Opening balance			2,000	C
3 July	Cheque 001254	750		1,250	C
4 July	Counter credit		800	2,050	C
5 July	Cheque 001259	25		2,025	C
8 July	Cheque 001260	690		1,335	C
14 July	Cheque 001261	364		971	C
16 July	Newberry & Co		2,650	3,621	C
18 July	Ellie Enderby Ltd		3,690	7,311	C
28 July	Cheque 001263	2,403		4,908	C
D = Debit C = Credit					

Cash book

Date 20-X	Details	Bank £	Date		Details	Bank £
1 July	Balance b/f	1,250	2 July	001259	Clifton Cars	25
2 July	Counter credit	800	6 July	001260	Arnbrook Ltd	690
15 July	Newberry & Co	2,650	12 July	001261	Harris Supplies	364
17 July	Ellie Enderby Ltd	3,690	27 July	001262	Wrenthorpe Town	1,267
18 July	Smithson	4,100	29 July	001263	Clifton Cars	2,403
25 July	Farnborough Supplies	315				

(a)   Reconcile the bank account with the cash book and complete the bank reconciliation statement below.

Bank reconciliation statement	£
Balance as per bank statement	
Add	
Total to add	
Less	
Total to subtract	
Balance as per cash book	

(7 marks)

(b)   Calculate the balance c/d as from the cash book in part (a).

£ [   ]

(1 mark)

Liam has just informed you that the transaction dated 6 July for a payment to Arnbrook Ltd was posted to the purchases account but it should have been posted to the drawings account.

(c)   Record the journal entries in the general ledger to correct this error.

Journal

Account name	Amount £	Debit	Credit

(4 marks)

Liam asks you to check an email to be sent to the bank enquiring about opening a deposit account.

(d)   Review the draft email and highlight **four** errors. Errors may be wrongly spelt, incorrectly used or technically incorrect.

Hi Mr Spencer

We have a curent account and would like enquire about opening a deposit account to transfer funds to on a regular basis.

Please can you provde me with some information as to how we can apply.

King regards

(4 marks)

Task 5: 12 marks

At Steinbeck Storage Solutions, management are very conscious of wanting to ensure they promote sustainability. You are asked to look at the following list.

(a)   Identify which **four** of the following would improve sustainability.

(a) Providing the time off for a member of staff to attend an AAT course	
(b) Sponsoring a local charity bike ride	
(c) Buying supplies from the cheapest supplier possible	
(d) Recycling packaging used on deliveries	
(e) Restricting the use of the internet at work for social networking	
(f) Allowing staff time off to volunteer at the local school summer fayre	
(g) Running the heating at a low level all year	

(4 marks)

Steinbeck Storage Solutions will be funding your AAT training and thought it would be useful for you to start to have a look at VAT entries. You have been provided with a summary of the transactions in the VAT control account:

(b)   Identify whether the transactions will be debits or credits in the VAT Control Account.

Transactions	Amount £	Debit	Credit
VAT amount in the discounts received day book	560		
VAT amount in the discounts allowed day book	2800		
VAT refund received from HM Revenue and Customs	3100		
VAT total in the purchase returns day book	970		
VAT total in the sales day book	6700		
VAT on cash sales	3006		

(6 marks)

The following month, your colleague Maria tells you that the debit balance on the VAT control account is £15,410 and the credit balance is £26,740. Maria informs you that credit customer Jepson Ltd are unable to pay the balance remaining on their account of £1,980 including VAT.

(c)   Calculate the amount of VAT relating to the irrecoverable debt.

£ [   ]

(1 mark)

(d)   Calculate the closing balance on the VAT account following the adjustment in (c) above.

£ [   ]

(1 mark)

Task 6: 24 marks

Maria asks you to calculate the figures within the manufacturing account using the information provided:

Opening inventory of work-in-progress	45,600
Closing inventory of raw materials	18,000
Direct labour	74,000
Opening inventory of finished goods	51,369
Closing inventory of finished goods	49,333
Opening inventory of raw materials	32,606
Purchase of raw materials	68,934
Closing inventory of work-in-progress	47,412
Manufacturing overheads	24,600

(a)   Using the information above, calculate the following:

Manufacturing cost	
Direct cost	
Cost of goods manufactured	
Cost of goods sold	
Direct materials used	

(10 marks)

(b)   In the box below, write a short report for non-finance staff containing:
- A brief introduction outlining the areas you will be covering in the report
- An explanation of the difference between raw materials and work-in-progress with an example
- An explanation of the difference between the direct cost and the manufacturing cost
- A description of how direct materials is calculated

Your report must be clear and structured appropriately.

(14 marks)

Task 7: 12 marks

Liam provides you with a list of account balances from the general ledger accounts and asks you to complete the trial balance.

(a) Enter the amounts into either the debit or credit column and total each column.

Account name	Amount £	Debit £	Credit £
Rent received	3,500		
Capital	8,000		
Sales	46,987		
Bank interest received	23		
Purchases	14,013		
Sales returns	2,017		
Purchase returns	578		
Discount allowed	3,654		
Discount received	2,145		
Sales Ledger Control	28,950		
Purchase Ledger Control	6,970		
Equipment	20,442		
Loan	2,400		
General expenses	8,047		
VAT owed to HMRC	6,520		
TOTAL			

(8 marks)

Steinbeck Storage Solutions pays its employees monthly and maintains a wages control account. A summary of last month's payroll transactions is shown below:

Item	£
Gross wages	9,240
Income tax	1,201
Employees' National Insurance contributions	997
Employer's National Insurance contributions	1,275
Employees' pension contributions	554
Employer's pension contributions	554

(b) Record the wages expense.

Account name	Amount £	Debit	Credit
Wages expense			
Wages control			

(2 marks)

(c) Record the HM Revenue and Customs liability.

Account name	Amount £	Debit	Credit
Wages control			
HM Revenue and Customs			

(2 marks)

(d) Record the pension fund liability.

Account name	Amount £	Debit	Credit
Wages control			
Pension fund			

(2 marks)

(e) Record the net wages paid to the employees.

Account name	Amount £	Debit	Credit
Wages control (Net pay)			
Bank			

(2 marks)

Practice
synoptic
assessment 4

Information

The total time for this practice assessment is 2 hours.

The total marks for this practice assessment is 100.

The marks for each sub-task are shown alongside the task.

Read the scenario carefully before attempting the questions.

Scenario

The tasks are set in a business situation where the following conditions apply:

- You are employed as an accounts assistant in the finance function at Carlton Cycles.

- The finance function includes the financial and management accounting teams.

- Carlton Cycles uses a manual bookkeeping system.

- Double entry takes place in the general ledger. Individual accounts of trade receivables and trade payables are kept in the sales and purchases ledger as subsidiary accounts.

- The cash book and petty cash book should be treated as part of the double entry system unless the task instructions state otherwise.

- The VAT rate is 20%.

Task 1: 12 marks

You work from 09.00 to 17.00, Monday to Friday of each week. Each finance period is four weeks in duration so you plan your work in a four week cycle.

The work schedules below show the days when routine tasks must be completed and the amount of time each task takes to complete. It is very important that you complete the management accounts tasks by the end of the identified day and the financial accounts tasks by the day and time indicated.

Monthly work schedule – management accounts					
	Monday	**Tuesday**	**Wednesday**	**Thursday**	**Friday**
Week 1	Variance analysis (2 hours)		Cost coding (3 hours)		
Week 2	Labour cost report (1 hour)	Labour cost report (1 hour)	Labour cost report (1 hour)		
Week 3	Data gathering (2 hours)	Material cost report (2 hours)	Product cost analysis (1 hour)	Product cost analysis (1 hour)	
Week 4	Data gathering (2 hours)			Budget report (2 hours)	Variance analysis (1 hour)

Weekly work schedule – financial accounts			
Task	**Task to be completed each week by:**		**Task duration**
	Day	**Time**	
Contact customers with outstanding debts	Monday	12.00	1 hour
Complete bank reconciliation	Wednesday	16:00	1 hour
Process purchase invoices	Tuesday	15:00	2 hours
Check emails and post cheques received	Every day	12.00	1 hour
Prepare payments to suppliers with remittance advices	Thursday	13:00	2 hours
Transfer entries from day books to ledgers	Friday	15:00	2 hours
Reconcile supplier statements with purchase ledger	Wednesday	14:00	2 hours
Process sales invoices	Tuesday	16.00	2 hours

You are planning your work at the start of the day on Tuesday of week 2. You have been asked to complete a non-routine cash book task by 10am and lunch should be taken at 12pm to 1pm.

(a) Complete your to-do list for today, Tuesday of week 2. Refer to the management and financial accounts schedules and list the tasks in order of completion in the table set out below. Write the task descriptions in the column on the right.

Choose from the following tasks:

Product cost analysis	Cash book
Budget report	Cost coding
Process purchase invoices	Variance analysis
Complete bank reconciliation	Lunch
Labour cost report	Process sales invoices
Data gathering	Material cost report

Transfer entries from day books to ledgers

Check emails and post cheques received

Contact customers with outstanding debts

Prepare payments to suppliers with remittance advices

Reconcile supplier statements with purchase ledger

Tuesday, week 2 to-do list (in order of completion)	
Task 1 09.00 -10.00	
Task 2 10.00 -11.00	
Task 3 11.00 -12.00	
Task 4 12.00 -13.00	
Task 5 13.00 -14.00	
Task 6 14.00 -15.00	
Task 7 15.00 -16.00	
Task 8 16.00 -17.00	

(8 marks)

You are often asked to complete non-routine tasks. However, two days in each of the four week cycles you are too busy with routine tasks to accept non-routine work.

(b)   Identify on which days and in which week they fall in that you will be the busiest with routine tasks from the management and financial accounts schedules. Enter your answers into the table below.

Week number	Day of the week

Week number	Day of the week

(4 marks)

Task 2: 12 marks

The three situations below highlight breaches of ethical principles in the workplace.

(a)   Complete the table by entering the fundamental principle which is breached in each case. Choose from the following principles:

Integrity

Objectivity

Confidentiality

A colleague uses some of the stamps purchased for the business to post her own personal mail	
The payroll assistant is heard in the local supermarket discussing colleagues pay rates	
The manager finds he is faced with a conflict of interest: his best friend's son is on the shortlist for a job and he is on the interviewing panel	

(3 marks)

During meetings Lorraine struggles to contribute when asked to complete work as a team. You decide to help Lorraine develop the skills essential to her role.

(b)   Which **four** of the skills/characteristics below demonstrate effective team work?

(a)	Everybody is talking over each other	
(b)	People take it in turns to put their ideas forward	
(c)	Listening to other's views	
(d)	Making eye contact with the person talking	
(e)	Checking your mobile phone for an urgent call	
(f)	Going ahead and completing work without consulting the team	
(g)	Not listening to other people's views	
(h)	Sharing the workload	

(4 marks)

(c)   Match the task with the job role.

(5 marks)

Task

Prepare sales invoices

Prepare remittance advices to send to suppliers

Update the cash book

Sales target reports

Production timings for the bikes to be delivered on time

Job role

Sales Manager

Sales Ledger Assistant

Production Manager

Cashier

Purchase Ledger Assistant

Task 3: 12 marks

Your line manager gives you the totals from the discount allowed day book.

Discount allowed day book

Details	Total £	VAT £	Net £
Totals	432	72	360

(a)   What will the entries be in the general ledger?

Account name	Amount £	Debit	Credit

(3 marks)

One of the customers offered discount, was Sky Ltd. They were issued a credit note for £60 plus VAT.

(b)   Record the journal entry to be made into the sales ledger account of Sky Ltd.

Account name	Amount £	Debit	Credit

(1 mark)

Your line manager gives you the totals from the discount received day book.

Discount received day book

Details	Total £	VAT £	Net £
Totals	1,080	180	900

(c)   What will the entries be in the general ledger?

Account name	Amount £	Debit	Credit

(3 marks)

One of the suppliers, Radford Supplies, offered Carlton Cycles a discount. They issued us a credit note for £170 plus VAT.

(d) Record the journal entry to be made into the purchase ledger account of Radford Supplies.

Account name	Amount £	Debit £	Credit £

(1 mark)

At Carlton Cycles a range of payment methods are used.

(e) Match each situation with the most appropriate payment method below:

(4 marks)

Situation

Making regular monthly payments for a telephone bill for varying amounts each month

Making a payment by post to pay for an advert in the local newspaper

Making regular monthly payments for rent for the same value each month

Making a payment via the internet to pay for vehicle tax

Choice of answers

Standing order

Debit card

Cheque

Direct debit

Task 4: 16 marks

At the end of July you have partially prepared Carlton Cycles sales ledger control account, as shown below.

Sales ledger control

Details	Amount £	Details	Amount £
Balance b/f	16,740	Bank	6,800

You now have the totals of the sales and sales returns day books and must record the appropriate amounts in the sales ledger control account

Sales day book extract

Date 20-X	Details	Total £	VAT £	Net £
July	Total	27,552	4,592	22,960

Sales returns day book extract

Date 20-X	Details	Total £	VAT £	Net £
July	Total	4,824	804	4,020

(a) What will the entries be into the sales ledger control account?

	Amount £	Debit	Credit
Entry from the sales day book			
Entry from the sales returns day book			

(4 marks)

(b) What will the balance carried down on the sales ledger control account be?

Amount £	Debit	Credit

(2 marks)

(c) Review the list of transactions to be posted into the purchase ledger control account and select whether they are debits or credits in the purchase ledger control account.

	Amount £	Debit	Credit
Balance of the credit suppliers at 1 July	8,400		
Payments made to credit suppliers	2,746		
Goods returned to credit suppliers	216		
Discount received	569		
Goods bought on credit	7,707		

(5 marks)

(d) What will be the balance brought down on 1 August on the above account?

£ [   ]

(1 mark)

Your manager, Mike, informs you that they would like to increase their credit limit to £5,500 with the supplier Radford Supplies if possible.

(e) Review the draft email and highlight **four** errors. Errors may be wrongly spelt, incorrectly used or technically incorrect.

> Hi Rachid,
>
> We regullary purchase goods on credit from you and our credit limit is currently £3,000. We would like to place a large order an would like to know if it is possible for our credit limit to be increased to £5,050.
>
> If you have any queres or would like to discuss this further please do not hesitate to contact me.
>
> Kind regards

(4 marks)

Task 5: 12 marks

Carlton Cycles are reviewing their sustainability policy.

(a) Select which areas of sustainability the following statements refer to:

	Social	Environmental
Allowing staff to volunteer in the community		
Reduce the quantity of printing		
Run a cycle to work scheme		
The use of fuel efficient cars		
Donation of profits to charity		
Energy saving schemes		

(3 marks)

Mike wants you to become more experienced in preparing the variance reports. You have been asked to calculate variances based on the monthly variance report of budgeted and actual income and costs. Any variance in excess of 5% of the budget is thought to be significant and should be reported to your manager.

(b) Complete the table below by:
- Inserting the variance in £
- Inserting adverse of favourable
- Inserting significant or not significant

	Budget £	Actual £	Variance £	Adverse or Favourable	Significant/Not significant
Income	180,740	188,600			
Direct materials	23,642	23,010			
Direct labour	34,090	34,156			
Production overheads	55,111	58,906			
Administration overheads	19,800	16,066			
Selling and Distribution Overheads	9,630	9,450			

(9 marks)

Task 6: 24 marks

Carlton Cycles is wanting to calculate the unit cost for one of the types of bikes it makes. It needs to calculate an overhead absorption rate to apply to each unit. The methods it is considering are:

Per labour hour

Per machine hour

Per unit

Total factory activity forecast is as follows:

Machine hours	10,000
Labour hours	15,000
Units	80,000
Overheads	£240,000

(a) Complete the table below to show the possible overhead absorption rates that Carlton Cycles could use. Your answers should be to two decimal places.

	Machine hour	Labour hour	Unit
Overheads £			
Activity			
Absorption rate £			

(3 marks)

The following information relates to making one unit of output:

Material	6 units at £7 per unit
Labour	30 minutes at £16 per hour
Production time	24 minutes

(b) Complete the table below to calculate the total unit cost, using the three overhead absorption rates you have calculated in (a). Your answers should be to two decimal places.

Cost	Machine hour £	Labour hour £	Unit £
Material			
Labour			
Direct cost			
Overheads			
Total unit cost			

(12 marks)

(c) In the box below, write a short report for non-finance staff containing:

- A brief introduction outlining the areas you will be covering in the report
- An explanation of what overheads are, giving an example
- A description of what an overhead absorption rate is

Your report must be clear and structured appropriately.

(9 marks)

Task 7: 12 marks

You are assisting with the month end accounts. On 31 July a trial balance was extracted and did not balance. The debit column totalled £300,470 and the credit column totalled £301,457.

(a) What entry is needed in the suspense account to balance the trial balance?

Account name	Debit £	Credit £

(1 mark)

Your manager, Mike, tells you that an error has been found and relates to an entry made in the general ledger from the incorrectly totalled net column in the purchases day book shown below.

Purchases day book

Date 20-X	Details	Invoice number	Total	VAT	Net
28 July	Radford Supplies	INV364	1,056	176	880
29 July	Lutterworth plc	001256	3,168	528	2,640
30 July	Bramcote plc	0A124	4,080	680	3,400
30 July	Radford Supplies	INV380	3,174	529	2,645
	Totals		11,478	1,913	9,656

(b) Record the journal entry needed to remove the incorrect entry.

Account name	Debit £	Credit £

(1 mark)

(c) Record the journal entry needed to record the correct entry.

Account name	Debit £	Credit £

(1 mark)

(d) Record the journal entry needed to the suspense account.

Account name	Debit £	Credit £

(1 mark)

(e)   Show whether the errors below will cause an imbalance in the trial balance.

	Will cause an imbalance	Will not cause an imbalance
A cash sale of £203 has not been entered in the accounts		
A cash sale of £200 has been recorded in the cash book only		
The balance on the purchases account has been calculated incorrectly		
Wages paid of £2,543 has been debited to wages account and debited in the cash book		

(4 marks)

(f)   Identify the type of error for the following transactions.

	Error of original entry	Error of omission	Error of commission	Error of principle
Office expenses has been debited with £3,410. This should have been posted to the office furniture account				
Discount allowed of £36 has been recorded in the discount allowed account as £63				
A cash receipt from a customer has not been entered in the cash book or the sales ledger control account				
A purchase invoice for £600 for LJ & Son has been credited to the account of JL & Son				

(4 marks)

Answers to practice synoptic assessment 1

Task 1: 12 marks

(a)

Thursday, week 2 to-do list (in order of completion)	
Task 1 09.00 -10.00	Petty cash book
Task 2 10.00 -11.00	Labour cost report
Task 3 11.00 -12.00	Check emails and post cheques
Task 4 12.00 -13.00	Reconcile supplier statements with purchase ledger
Task 5 13.00 -14.00	Reconcile supplier statements with purchase ledger

Note: Can also accept Task 2 Check emails and post cheques and Task 3 labour cost report

(b)

Week number	Day of the week
1	Monday

(c) Petty cash book

Details	Amount £	Details	Amount £	VAT £	Stationery £	Postage £	Travel £
Balance b/f	150.00	Paper	15.60	2.60	13.00		
		Train fare	26.30				26.30
		Stamps	9.80			9.80	
		Balance c/d	98.30				
Total	150.00	Totals	150.00	2.60	13.00	9.80	26.30

(d) General ledger

Account name	Amount £	Debit	Credit
VAT	2.60	✔	
Stationery	13.00	✔	
Postage	9.80	✔	
Travel	26.30	✔	

Task 2: 12 marks

(a)

Management Accountant	Financial Accountant
Deals with future income and costs	Deals with financial transactions that have already happened
Prepares budgets	Prepares the financial statements including tax and VAT

(b)

Task	Job role
Sales figures report for each sales advisor	Sales Manager
Production schedule for the factory	Human Resources Assistant
Process invoices received from suppliers	Sales Ledger Assistant
Process cheques received	Production Manager
Prepare employee contracts	Cashier
	Purchase Ledger Assistant

Connections:
- Sales figures report for each sales advisor → Sales Manager
- Production schedule for the factory → Production Manager
- Process invoices received from suppliers → Purchase Ledger Assistant
- Process cheques received → Cashier
- Prepare employee contracts → Human Resources Assistant

(c)

Good communication skills	✔
Must have accountancy qualifications	
Must complete their work before other members of the group	
Be able to work to deadlines	✔
Be able to help others in the group when required	✔

Task 3: 12 marks

(a)   Errors on purchase invoice: Goods total is incorrect. It should be £420.00 and the VAT has been deducted instead of added.

Errors on purchase credit note: wrong trade discount percentage applied (it states 20% but 10% has been applied) and the number of items returned do not match (quantity states 12 but reason for credit states 2.)

(b)   **(c)**   Purchases day book

Date 20-X	Details	Invoice number	Total	VAT	Net
29 July	PWS Supplies	INV4514	£149.32	£24.88	£124.44
30 July	Working Products	269852	£592.92	£98.82	£494.10
	Totals		**£742.24**	**£123.70**	**£618.54**

Task 4: 16 marks

(a)

Account name	Amount £	Debit	Credit
Entry from the purchase day book	5,448		✔
Entry from the purchase returns day book	960	✔	

(b)

Amount £	Debit	Credit
5,268		✔

Workings: £5,410 + £5,448 − £4,630 − £960 = £5,268

(c)

Reconciliation statement	Amount £
Sales ledger control account balance	29,463
Total of the sales ledger balances	29,016
Difference	447

(d)   A receipt was entered twice in a customer's account in the sales ledger

An invoice was entered twice in the sales ledger control account

(e)

> Hi Mr Jones
>
> Our **purchase** ledger shows an outstanding balance on your account of **£9,500**. This has been **outstanding** for 60 days which has **exceeded** our 30 day payment terms.
>
> Please can you arrange **payment** as soon as **possible** and if you have any questions or queries please do not hesitate to contact me.
>
> Kind regards

Task 5: 12 marks

(a)

	Social	Environmental
Using resources that can be reused		✔
Supporting colleagues	✔	
Reduction of emissions		✔
Reduce the quantity of printing		✔
Donation of profits to charity	✔	
Energy saving schemes		✔

(b)   **Event cost performance report**

Cost	Budget £	Actual £	Variance £	Adverse/ Favourable	Significant/ Not significant
Entertainment	800.00	835.00	35.00	Adverse	Significant
Food	600.00	623.00	23.00	Adverse	Not significant

Task 6: 24 Marks

(a)

Employee name	Hours worked	Units produced	Basic wage £	Bonus £	Gross wage £
Lukasz	36	370	284.40	27.60	312.00
Samuel	36	320	284.40	0.00	284.40
James	36	330	284.40	3.60	288.00
Tom	36	344	284.40	12.00	296.40

(b)

> This report will cover an explanation of labour costs with JYB Supplies.
>
> Time-rate pay is based on the number of hours worked. For example if an employee worked 37 hours a week with an hourly rate of £8.00, pay for the week would be £296.
>
> Piecework is payments per unit produced. For example employees in a factory are paid for each item they make. If an employee gets paid £0.95 per unit produced and they produced 300 units this week, total pay would be £285.
>
> Other types of pay include overtime when an employee works over the standard weekly hours, they may be paid a higher overtime rate for hours over and above the standard working weekly hours.
>
> Some businesses will pay a bonus if employees meet certain targets. This is an additional payment on top of their usual pay.

Task 7: 12 Marks

(a)

Account name	Amount £	Debit £	Credit £
Bank (overdraft)	2,600		2,600
Sales	28,704		28,704
Purchases	16,256	16,256	
Sales returns	2,900	2,900	
Purchase returns	680		680
Office equipment	9,300	9,300	
Administration expenses	1,008	1,008	
Sales ledger control	12,580	12,580	
Purchase ledger control	4,630		4,630
Capital	5,680		5,680
Petty cash	250	250	
Total		42,294	42,294

(b)   **Journal**

Account name	Amount £	Debit	Credit
Sales ledger control	1,440		✔
Irrecoverable debt	1,200	✔	
VAT	240	✔	

(c)

Account name	Amount £	Debit	Credit
Timber plc	1,440		✔

(d)   **Fairtown Ltd**

Date 20-X	Details	Amount £	Date	Details	Amount £
14 July	Credit note CN41	500.00	1 July	Balance b/f	2,000.00
16 July	Bank	700.00	12 July	Invoice 3245	1,000.00
31 July	Balance c/d	1,800.00			
		3,000.00			3,000.00
			1 Aug	Balance b/d	1,800.00

Smithson Taylor

Date 20-X	Details	Amount £	Date	Details	Amount £
11 July	Credit note 25	103.40	1 July	Balance b/f	645.00
20 July	Bank	645.00	10 July	Invoice INV457	475.30
31 July	Balance c/d	371.90			
		1,120.30			1,120.30
			1 Aug	Balance b/d	371.90

Answers to
practice
synoptic
assessment 2

Task 1: 12 marks

(a)   (c)   Jim has finished producing the sales invoices and knows that Jasmin is struggling to contact all the customers who have not paid on time. Jim checks with his manager to see if he can offer to help Jasmin.

(b)

(a)	Tax computation	✔
(b)	VAT return	✔
(c)	Production schedule	
(d)	Coding invoices	✔
(e)	Issuing contracts to new staff	

(c)

(a)	Data protection	✔
(b)	Whistleblowing	✔
(c)	Quality control in the production department	
(d)	Manual handling for lifting heavy packages	

(d)   **(1)**   Errors on the purchase invoice are as follows:

- Quantity on invoice for first item does not match the purchase order.
- Product code for the second item is incorrect
- The 15% discount has been incorrectly calculated.

(2)   Errors on the purchase invoice are as follows:

- Wrong product invoiced
- Quantity for the second item is incorrect
- The total invoice amount is incorrect because VAT has been deducted instead of added on

Task 2: 12 marks

(a)

(a)	Stock valuation	
(b)	Bank reconciliation	✔
(c)	Banking cheques received	✔
(d)	Be able to work to deadlines	

(b)   (a)   Customers pay earlier

(c)

A sustainability policy including details of the new car sharing scheme		**smooth running of an organisation**
Petty cash procedures		
Make sure credit customers pay on time		
Electronic planner of staff holidays to ensure staff absences are evenly spread		**improves solvency**
Pay the PAYE and National Insurance Contributions to HMRC		
Pay VAT due		**is a legal requirement**
Avoid having to pay overtime to staff		

(d)

(a)	Enrol onto AAT Level 3	✔
(b)	Complete an excel online course	✔
(c)	Attend a tax seminar	
(d)	Complete a Microsoft word course	

Task 3: 12 marks

(a) **Cash book – debit side**

Details	Cash £	Bank £	VAT £	Trade Receivables £	Cash sales £
Balance b/f	254.36				
L Harris Ltd		2410.00		2410.00	
Michelle Proctor		980.60		980.60	
Askham Ltd	66.00		11.00		55.00

(b) £320.36

(c) £1,118.60

Workings: £450.60 + £4,058.60 – £2,410.00 – £980.60 = £1,118.60

(d)

Credit	
Debit	✔

(e)

	Debit	Credit
Payment to HMRC for VAT of £3,484		✔
Debit card receipt of £540 from a trade receivable	✔	
Receipt from HRMC for £410	✔	
Debit card payment of £140 to a trade payable		✔

Task 4: 16 marks

(a)   (1)   **Journal**

Account name	Amount £	Debit	Credit
Irrecoverable debts	2,982.75	✔	
VAT	596.55	✔	
Sales ledger control	3,579.30		✔

(2)

	Will cause an imbalance	Will not cause an imbalance
The vehicle expenses have been debited with £12,451. This should have been posted to the vehicles account		✔
The balance on the rent received account has been calculated incorrectly	✔	
Rent received of £565 has been recorded as £656 in the rent received account only	✔	
Interest received has been posted to the rent received account		✔

(b)   (1)

Account name	Original balance £	Debit	Credit
Purchase returns	2,906		✔
VAT Control (owing to HMRC)	5,680		✔
Bank interest received	58		✔
Bank (overdrawn bank balance)	3,970		✔
Sales returns	585	✔	

(2)

Account name	Debit	Credit
Totals	103,234	103,234

(3)

> **Email**
>
> Hi Mr Templin
>
> Our sales ledger shows an **outstanding** balance on your account of £10,245. This has been outstanding for 90 days which has **exceeded** our 30 day payment terms.
>
> Please can you **arrange** payments as soon as possible and if you have any queries please do not hesitate to contact me.
>
> Kind regards

Task 5: 12 Marks

(a)

(a) Driving for two hours to attend a meeting	
(b) Holding the meeting via skype	✔
(c) Using recyclable plant holders	✔
(d) Ensuring customers are treated equally	
(e) Promote a cycle to work scheme	✔
(f) Print all accounting correspondence and file in the accounts office	

(b)

Name	Hours worked	Basic wage £	Overtime £	Gross wage £
Sam Stepton	40	511.20	84.80	596.00
Tanveer Mahmood	42	511.20	127.20	638.40
Kelly Johnstone	35	497.00	0.00	497.00

Task 6: 24 marks

(a)

Method	Cost of issue £	Closing inventory £
FIFO	654.00	152.00
LIFO	662.00	144.00
AVCO	659.45	146.55

Workings:

FIFO Cost of issue:

150 pots x £3.60 = £540.00

(180 pots – 150 pots = 30 pots) 30 pots x £3.80 = £114.00

£540.00 + £114.00 = £654.00

FIFO Closing Inventory:

Number of pots left (70 pots – 30 already issued = 40 pots left)

40 pots x £3.80 = £152.00

LIFO Cost of issue:

70 pots x £3.80 = £266.00

(180 pots – 70 pots = 110 pots) 110 pots x £3.60 = £396.00

£266.00 + £396.00 = £662.00

LIFO Closing Inventory:

Number of pots left (150 pots − 110 already issued = 40 pots left)

40 pots x £3.60 = £144.00

AVCO Cost of issue:

Total number of pots = 150 pots + 70 pots = 220 pots

Total value of pots:

150 pots x £3.60 = £540.00

70 pots x £3.60 = £266.00

£540.00 + £266.00 = £806.00

£806.00 / 220 pots = £3.6636363636 (leave this figure in your calculator) x 180 = £659.45

AVCO Closing Inventory:

£806.00 − £659.45 = £146.55

(b)

REPORT

This report will cover an explanation of the three different inventory valuation methods. Because the prices of items change day to day, this affects the valuation of both issues and closing inventory.

When issuing inventory using FIFO (First in first out) inventory is issued using the oldest purchase price. Therefore items left are at the most recent purchase price and the closing inventory is valued at this most recent purchase price.

When issuing inventory using LIFO (Last in first out) inventory is issued using the most recent purchase price. Therefore items left are at the oldest purchase price and the closing inventory is valued at the oldest purchase price.

AVCO (Average cost) is calculated by using the following formula:

total cost of goods held/number of items held.

This gives the average cost of the inventory held.

Task 7: 12 Marks

(a)   (1)

Account name	Amount £	Debit	Credit
Pots	2,590	✔	
Plants	8,480	✔	
VAT	2,214	✔	
Purchase ledger control	13,284		✔

(2)

Account name	Amount £	Debit	Credit
Midway Suppliers	876		✔
Peterborough Plants	11,436		✔
Skegby Suppliers	972		✔

(b)   **Sales day book extract**

	Amount £	Debit	Credit
Entry from the sales day book	19,764	✔	
Entry from the sales returns day book	3,720		✔

Answers to practice synoptic assessment 3

Task 1: 12 marks

(a)

(a)	Reporting requirements of corporation tax	
(b)	Telephone training	✔
(c)	Microsoft Word training	✔
(d)	Understanding PAYE	
(e)	Conflict resolution	

(b)

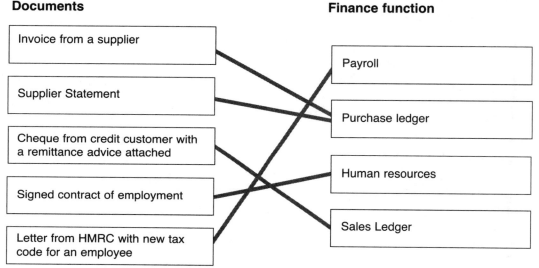

Documents

- Invoice from a supplier
- Supplier Statement
- Cheque from credit customer with a remittance advice attached
- Signed contract of employment
- Letter from HMRC with new tax code for an employee

Finance function

- Payroll
- Purchase ledger
- Human resources
- Sales Ledger

(c)   (b)   Purchase Returns Day Book

(d)

Date 20-X	Details	Credit note number	Total £	VAT £	Net £
30 July	Woodborough Ltd	CN067	168.00	28.00	140.00
31 July	LYB Newton & Son Ltd	01240	940.03	156.67	783.36
	Totals		1,108.03	184.67	923.36

(e)   **Document**

Day book

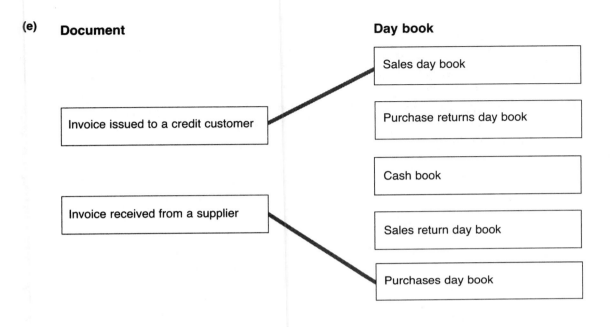

Invoice issued to a credit customer

Invoice received from a supplier

Sales day book

Purchase returns day book

Cash book

Sales return day book

Purchases day book

Task 2: 12 marks

(a) (c) A password that combines letters, numbers, uppercase and special characters

(b) (a) Guidance for lifting heavy items

(c) (d) Refer to your supervisor as this is confidential information you are being asked to disclose

(d)

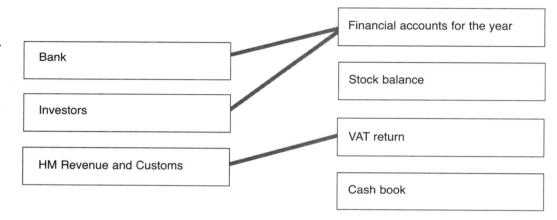

Stakeholder   **Accounting information**

Bank

Investors

HM Revenue and Customs

Financial accounts for the year

Stock balance

VAT return

Cash book

(e)

(a)	Integrity	✔
(b)	Objectivity	✔
(c)	Confidence	
(d)	Effectiveness	
(e)	Professional competence	✔
(f)	Motivation	

(f)

(a)	Producing year-end accounts	✔
(b)	Preparing budgets	
(c)	Preparing VAT returns	✔
(d)	Calculating the costs of products	
(e)	Preparing tax computations	✔
(f)	Preparing labour cost analysis	

Task 3: 12 marks

(a)

INVOICE				**Steinbeck Storage Solutions**			

53 Maclean Industrial Estate
Beeston, BH6 5RS

VAT Reg GB 870 1247 78

invoice to

Mapperley Pine Centre
Carlton Road
Nottingham
MJ5 6LK

invoice no   1240

date/tax point   5 March 20-X

Product Code	Description	Quantity	Price	Unit	Total	Discount	Net
UPSK2563	Unfinished pine shelf kit	72	£6.00	each			
PB2410	Pine brackets	12	£3.20	each	£470.40	10%	£423.36

terms
Net monthly
Carriage paid
E & OE
6% prompt payment discount for payment within 7 days

goods total	£423.36
VAT	£84.67
TOTAL	£508.03

(b)   £477.55

Workings:

Goods total £423.36 x 0.06 (prompt payment discount) = £25.40
£25.40 x 0.20 VAT = £5.08
£25.40 + £5.08 = £30.48 discount
£508.03 Invoice total – £30.48 discount = £477.55

(c)

Credit note 066	Invoice 601	**Credit note 064**
Invoice 658	Credit note 050	Balance b/f
Invoice 701	**Invoice 740**	Bank

Task 4: 16 marks

(b)

Bank reconciliation statement	£
Balance as per bank statement	4908
Add	
Smithson	4100
Farnborough Supplies	315
Total to add	4415
Less	
Wrenthorpe Town	1267
Total to subtract	1267
Balance as per cash book	8056

(b)   £8,056

(c)   Journal

Account name	Amount £	Debit	Credit
Drawings	690	✔	
Purchases	690		✔

(d)

Hi Mr Spencer

We have a **current** account and would like **to** enquire about opening a deposit account to transfer funds to on a regular basis.

Please can you **provide** me with some information as to how we can apply.

Kind regards

Task 5: 12 marks

(a)

(a)	Providing the time off for a member of staff to attend an AAT course	
(b)	Sponsoring a local charity bike ride	✔
(c)	Buying supplies from the cheapest supplier possible	
(d)	Recycling packaging used on deliveries	✔
(e)	Restricting the use of the internet at work for social networking	
(f)	Allowing staff time off to volunteer at the local school summer fayre	✔
(g)	Running the heating at a low level all year	✔

(b)

Transactions	Amount £	Debit	Credit
VAT amount in the discounts received day book	560		✔
VAT amount in the discounts allowed day book	2800	✔	
VAT refund received from HM Revenue and Customs	3100	✔	
VAT total in the purchase returns day book	970		✔
VAT total in the sales day book	6700		✔
VAT on cash sales	3006		✔

(c)   £330
  Workings: £1,980 / 6 = £330

(d)   £11,000
  Workings: £26,740 – £15,410 – £330 = £11,000

Task 6: 24 marks

(a)

Manufacturing cost	£182,140
Direct cost	£157,540
Cost of goods manufactured	£180,328
Cost of goods sold	£182,364
Direct materials used	£83,540

Workings:

Opening inventory of raw materials	32606
Purchase of raw materials	+68934
Closing inventory of raw materials	−18000
DIRECT MATERIALS	**=83540**
Direct labour	+74000
DIRECT COST	**=157540**
Manufacturing overheads	+24600
MANUFACTURING COST	**=182140**
Opening inventory of work-in-progress	+45600
Closing inventory of work-in-progress	−47412
COST OF GOODS MANUFACTURED	**=180328**
Opening inventory of finished goods	+51369
Closing inventory of finished goods	−49333
COST OF GOODS SOLD	**=182364**

(b)

> **REPORT**
>
> This report will cover an explanation of the manufacturing account format.
>
> Raw materials are the parts used to produce a product. For example the pieces of wood used to make the cabinets. When the cabinets are partially completed this is known as work-in-progress because the cabinets are not ready to be sold.
>
> Direct costs are the costs that can be directly identified with the units of output. This is made up of materials and labour. The manufacturing cost is made up of the direct costs plus any manufacturing overheads.
>
> Direct materials is calculated as follows: opening inventory of raw materials, plus materials purchased, minus closing inventory of raw materials.

Task 7: 12 marks

(a)

Account name	Amount £	Debit £	Credit £
Rent received	3,500		3,500
Capital	8,000		8,000
Sales	46,987		46,987
Bank interest received	23		23
Purchases	14,013	14,013	
Sales returns	2,017	2,017	
Purchase returns	578		578
Discount allowed	3,654	3,654	
Discount received	2,145		2,145
Sales Ledger Control	28,950	28,950	
Purchase Ledger Control	6,970		6,970
Equipment	20,442	20,442	
Loan	2,400		2,400
General expenses	8,047	8,047	
VAT owed to HMRC	6,520		6,520
TOTAL		77,123	77,123

(b)

Account name	Amount £	Debit	Credit
Wages expense	11,069	✔	
Wages control	11,069		✔

Workings: for Wages expense figure of £11,069

Gross wages £9,240 + Employer's National Insurance contributions £1,275 + Employer's pension contributions £554 = £11,069

(c)

Account name	Amount £	Debit	Credit
Wages control	3,473	✔	
HM Revenue and Customs	3,473		✔

Workings: for HM Revenue and Customs liability of £3,473

Income tax £1,201 + Employees' National Insurance contribution £997 + Employer's National Insurance contributions £1,275 = £3,473

(d)

Account name	Amount £	Debit	Credit
Wages control	1,108	✔	
Pension fund	1,108		✔

Workings: for Pension fund liability of £1,108

Employees' pension contributions £554 + Employer's pension contributions £554 = £1,108

(e)

Account name	Amount £	Debit	Credit
Wages control (Net pay)	6,488	✔	
Bank	6,488		✔

Workings: for Net wages paid to employees of £6,488

Gross wages £9,240 – Income Tax £1,201 – Employees' National Insurance contribution £997 – Employees' pension contributions £554 = £6,488

Task 2: 12 marks

(a)

A colleague uses some of the stamps purchased for the business to post her own personal mail	Integrity
The payroll assistant is heard in the local supermarket discussing colleagues pay rates	Confidentiality
The manager finds he is faced with a conflict of interest: his best friend's son is on the shortlist for a job and he is on the interviewing panel	Objectivity

(b)

(a)	Everybody is talking over each other	
(b)	People take it in turns to put their ideas forward	✔
(c)	Listening to other's views	✔
(d)	Making eye contact with the person talking	✔
(e)	Checking your mobile phone for an urgent call	
(f)	Going ahead and completing work without consulting the team	
(g)	Not listening to other people's views	
(h)	Sharing the workload	✔

(c)   **Task**   **Job role**

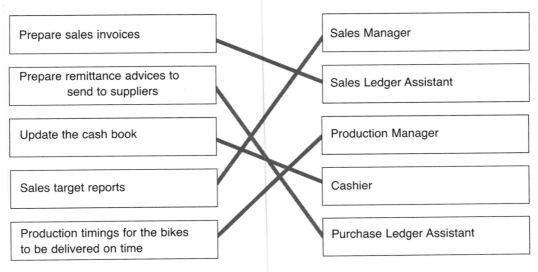

Task 3: 12 marks

(a)

Account name	Amount £	Debit	Credit
Discount allowed	360	✔	
VAT	72	✔	
Sales ledger control	432		✔

(b)

Account name	Amount £	Debit	Credit £
Sky Ltd	72		✔

(c)

Account name	Amount £	Debit	Credit
Discount received	900		✔
VAT	180		✔
Purchase ledger control	1,080	✔	

(d)

Account name	Amount £	Debit	Credit
Radford Supplies	204	✔	

(e)

Situation	Choice of answers
Making regular monthly payments for a telephone bill for varying amounts each month	Standing order
Making a payment by post to pay for an advert in the local newspaper	Debit card
Making regular monthly payments for rent for the same value each month	Cheque
Making a payment via the internet to pay for vehicle tax	Direct debit

Task 4: 16 marks

(a)

	Amount £	Debit	Credit
Entry from the sales day book	27,552	✔	
Entry from the sales returns day book	4,824		✔

(b)

Amount £	Debit	Credit
32,668	✔	

(c)

	Amount £	Debit	Credit
Balance of the credit suppliers at 1 July	8,400		✔
Payments made to credit suppliers	2,746	✔	
Goods returned to credit suppliers	216	✔	
Discount received	569	✔	
Goods bought on credit	7,707		✔

(d)   £12,576

Working:

£8,400 – £2,746 – £216 – £569 + £7,707 = £12,576

(e)

Hi Rachid,

We **regularly** purchase goods on credit from you and our credit limit is currently £3,000. We would like to place a large order **and** would like to know if it is possible for our credit limit to be increased to **£5,500**.

If you have any **queries** or would like to discuss this further please do not hesitate to contact me.

Kind regards

Task 5: 12 marks

(a)

	Social	Environmental
Allowing staff to volunteer in the community	✔	
Reduce the quantity of printing		✔
Run a cycle to work scheme		✔
The use of fuel efficient cars		✔
Donation of profits to charity	✔	
Energy saving schemes		✔

(b)

	Budget £	Actual £	Variance £	Adverse or Favourable	Significant/Not significant
Income	180,740	188,600	7,860	Favourable	not significant
Direct materials	23,642	23,010	632	Favourable	not significant
Direct labour	34,090	34,156	66	Adverse	not significant
Production overheads	55,111	58,906	3,795	Adverse	significant
Administration overheads	19,800	16,066	3,734	Favourable	significant
Selling and Distribution Overheads	9,630	9,450	180	Favourable	not significant

Task 6: 24 marks

(a)

	Machine hour	Labour hour	Unit
Overheads £	240,000	240,000	240,000
Activity	10,000	15,000	80,000
Absorption rate £	24.00	16.00	3.00

(b)

Cost	Machine hour £	Labour hour £	Unit £
Material	42.00	42.00	42.00
Labour	8.00	8.00	8.00
Direct cost	50.00	50.00	50.00
Overheads	9.60	8.00	3.00
Total unit cost	59.60	58.00	53.00

(c)

REPORT

This report will cover an explanation of overheads and overhead absorption rates.

An overhead is not directly related to the products being manufactured. There these are non-production costs known as indirect costs. For example rent paid on premises.

The overhead absorption rate is the cost of overheads charged to the cost units which pass through a specific department. For example with machine hours, an element of overheads will be charged to machine hours. With labour hours an element of overheads will be charged to labour hours.

Task 7: 12 marks

(a)

Account name	Debit £	Credit £
Suspense	987	

(b)

Account name	Debit £	Credit £
Purchases		9,656

(c)

Account name	Debit £	Credit £
Purchases	9,565	

(d)

Account name	Debit £	Credit £
Suspense	91	

(e)

	Will cause an imbalance	Will not cause an imbalance
A cash sale of £203 has not been entered in the accounts		✔
A cash sale of £200 has been recorded in the cash book only	✔	
The balance on the purchases account has been calculated incorrectly	✔	
Wages paid of £2,543 has been debited to wages account and debited in the cash book	✔	

(f)

	Error of original entry	Error of omission	Error of commission	Error of principle
Office expenses has been debited with £3,410. This should have been posted to the office furniture account				✔
Discount allowed of £36 has been recorded in the discount allowed account as £63	✔			
A cash receipt from customer has not been entered in the cash book or the sales ledger control account		✔		
A purchase invoice for £600 for LJ & Son has been credited to the account of JL & Son			✔	